MONA THE VAMPIRE

The Original MONA the VAMPIRE Book

Sonia Holleyman

Scholastic Canada Ltd.
Toronto New York London Auckland Sydney
Mexico City New Delhi Hong Kong

For Mum and Dad

and

Eva Louise Fowler

National Library of Canada Cataloguing in Publication Data
Holleyman, Sonia
The original Mona the vampire picture book
ISBN 0-439-98870-5
I. Title.
PZ7.H7246Or 2001 j823'.914 C2001-901047-8

This edition printed in 2001 by Scholastic Canada Ltd.,
175 Hillmount Road, Markham, Ontario, L6C 1Z7.

First published in Great Britain in 1990 by Orchard Books.

6 5 4 3 2 1 Printed in Canada 01 02 03 04 05

It was Friday evening. Mum had gone off to karate class and Dad was reading Mona an excellent bedtime story. It was full of wicked witches and ghostly ghouls; it made her eyes pop and her blood curdle. Mona loved it. So did her cat, Fang.

“I’d like to be a vampire!” thought Mona, as she was brushing her teeth. “I could hang upside down all night and never go to bed. And Fang could scare all the teachers at school . . .”

But Mona and Fang were soon fast asleep.

On Saturday morning, Mona was up bright and early; she had a busy day ahead. First she needed a vampire cape. The long curtains in the dining room were just the thing. Fang loved his new batwings.

Fang and Mona also played with Mum's makeup. Mona's plastic glow-in-the-dark fangs made her dribble a bit, but the overall effect was perfect.

"Behold Dracula's daughter!" she hissed.

Mum made them a special monstrous lunch. They had batwing soup, clammy-hammy sandwiches with ketchup, and squashed fly cake. Fang's favourites were the barbecued bat burgers.

Fang was learning fast. Mona took him to the end of the garden and taught him all the important things vampires need to know, like always wear clean underpants. Then they played hide-and-seek-a-vampire and suck-my-blood.

But even vampires are no match for a karate expert like Mum, so when she said, "I want your room tidied up as neat as a pin!" Mona did her best — with Fang's help.

On Monday morning, Mona helped Mum by making her own sandwiches. She liked lots of ketchup: it was so finger-licking, fang-watering good! She put her lunch box in her bag and buttoned Fang into her sweater. She was taking him to school.

Mona told her class all about vampires and showed them some special vampire tricks. No one would sit next to her any more.

Mona always looked forward to gym and playing on the apparatus. She practised tying all her special knots. Fang loved it; he had so much to learn.

When Mona painted a picture on the classroom wall, the teacher shouted, “Enough is enough! I cannot have that child in my class!”

She sent for the principal. “Enough is enough!” shouted the principal. “Something must be done!”

So Mona went to join the ballet class, to calm her down. Fang went too.

Mona and Fang taught the good little ballerinas some exciting new pointe work, but Mr. Kersley the teacher didn't like it one bit, and snapped, "Enough is enough!" Luckily for him, it was time to go home.

"Hurray!" shouted Mona and Fang. They didn't want to be calmed down.

Mona pedalled cheerfully homeward; vampires didn't do ballet anyway. Her cape flapped gaily behind her as she sped along. It was the perfect day for vampiring.

The wind began to whistle, and cold, dark rain began to fall. Mona decided to take a shortcut home, past the churchyard.

The storm grew worse. The lightning cast eerie vampire shadows, the thunder roared like a huge monster, and the wind shrieked like a witch on a broomstick.

The shrieking and the clamouring woke up the bats in the belfry. Mona pedalled faster.

Mona and Fang skidded around the corner and saw their house at the end of the street. It was a great relief. Even vampires get homesick.

And Mona was sick and tired. She stood miserably on the doorstep and called for Mum. Fang sneezed.

"Enough is enough!" said Mum firmly, and made hot chocolate for them all. Then Mona was given a nice warm bath and put straight to bed.

Mona had rather disturbed dreams that night. Wicked witches and ghostly ghouls came out to play: they had heard all about Mona the Vampire!

In the morning a rather pale Mona washed off all her makeup and tidied her room. She brushed the knots out of her hair and put away her fangs. “I won’t need these any more!” she said. Fang agreed. No more ketchup lunches and definitely no more bat-hanging from the ballet barre.

And that evening, when Mum was at karate,
Dad read Mona an excellent bedtime story . . .

But this time it was about space invaders.